TUESDAY
ME FIRE A RUBBER SUCTION ARROW AT DAD'S NOSE!
WEDNESDAY
ME BLOW SNEEZING POWDER AT DAD!
SNEEZING POWDER
HOLIDAYS
SATURDAY
ME GET MORE FEATHERS FOR MY RED INDIAN HEAD-DRESS!
SUNDAY
ME SET A BIG TACK ON DAD'S CHAIR!

To Derek Christmas 1987 from - Aunt Jean Uncle Ken & Allison All our love xxxx
KORKY'S MOUSE-CATCHING STALL
ROLL UP! ROLL UP! BUY YOUR MOUSE-CATCHING GEAR HERE!
EEK!
SPIDER-MOUSE NET
SCARE-A-MOUSE MASK
YE ANCIENT MOUSE CRUSHER (VERY RARE)
LONG-RANGE "MOUSE"-ILE
FLYING MOUSE-CATCHER (IDEAL FOR HIGH RISE FLATS)
MOUSE SWATTER
??
SOCK IN THE BOX (SURPRISE THE MICE)
?
ZZZ
ZZZ

THE
DANDY
BOOK
MOUSE GNASHERS
MODIFIED MOUSE-TRAP (IT'S A KNOCK-OUT)
STEP MISSING LADDER!
PIRANHAS
FREE CHEESE! COME AND GET IT!

Printed and Published in Great Britain by D. C. THOMSON & CO., LTD.,
185 Fleet Street, London, EC4A 2HS.

ISBN 0 85116 385 8

DINAH MO
ALL NICE GIRLS SHOULD LEARN TO PLAY THE PIANO, MO!
HUMPH!

I'D RATHER PLAY MY GUITAR!

KERANG!
WHAT ON EARTH!

KER-ANG!
OOH!

GIVE ME THAT!
BAH!

I'M GOING TO LOCK THIS GUITAR AWAY!
MUM IS A SPOIL-SPORT!

NOW BEHAVE YOURSELF. THE VICAR IS COMING ROUND THIS AFTERNOON!

GOSH! THE VICAR'S VISIT MIGHT NOT BE A BAD THING AFTER ALL. MUM IS BAKING SOME LOVELY CAKES!

RIGHT! I'LL JUST GO AND HAVE A QUICK WASH!
SLURP!

A little later—
WHERE ARE MY CAKES?

YOU NAUGHTY GIRL, MO! I'M GOING TO LOCK YOU IN YOUR ROOM!

Just then—
KNOCK! KNOCK!
THERE'S SOMEONE AT THE DOOR!

OH, IT'S YOU, VICAR!

I'VE COME TO ASK YOU IF YOU HAVE ANYTHING TO DONATE TO THE CHURCH SUMMER FETE!

ER, WELL! I WAS GOING TO GIVE YOU SOME CAKES, BUT I HAD A DISASTER WITH THE BAKING.

NEVER MIND! I HAVE SOME JUMBLE IN THE CUPBOARD!

I SAY! DOES SOMEONE PLAY THE GUITAR HERE?
ME! I'LL SHOW YOU!

TWING! TWANG!
VERY GOOD!

RIGHT! HERE'S MY PLAN!

At the summer fete—
SUPER! MO AND CO ARE RAISING MONEY FOR THE CHURCH FUNDS WITH THEIR MUSIC!
SUMMER FETE
TWING TWANG
PLINK PLONK
OIL DRUM
TEA CHEST

DANDY HORSELAUGHS

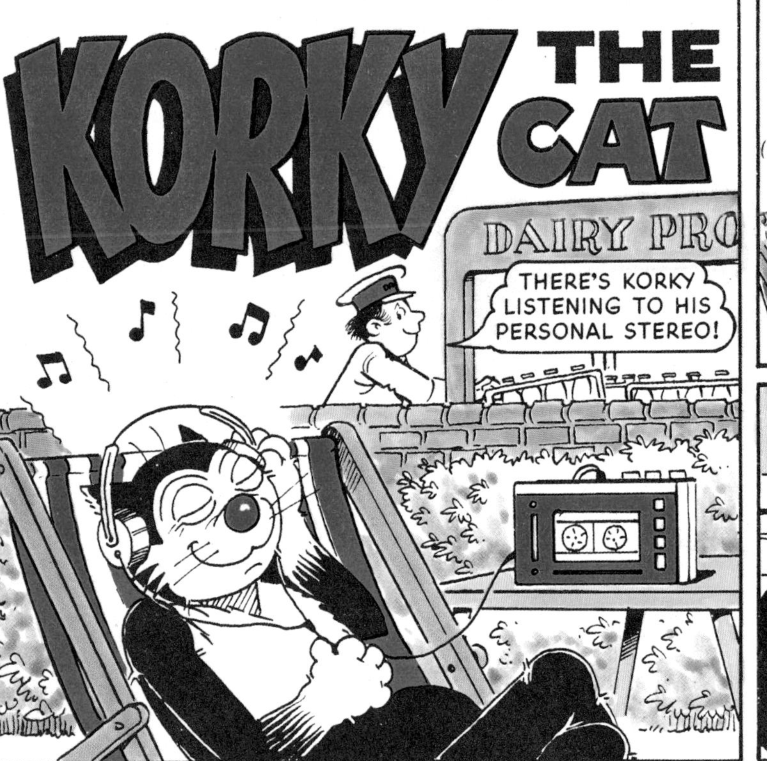
KORKY THE CAT
DAIRY PRO
THERE'S KORKY LISTENING TO HIS PERSONAL STEREO!

HOW MANY BOTTLES TODAY, KORKY?
EH? OH — SORRY! TWO PLEASE!

I'LL POP THEM IN THE FRIDGE!

NOW TO LISTEN TO THE REST OF MY TAPE!

HEY! STOP USING MY HEADPHONES AS A SWING!

CRUMBS! IT'S KORKY BACK ALREADY! RUN FOR IT, LADS!
CRASH!
BUMP!

YOU'VE BROKEN MY PERSONAL STEREO SET, YOU MENACES!
SWIPE!

THERE! THAT'S THE LAST ONE ROUNDED UP!

RADIO & T.V. REPA
WHERE'S KORKY TAKING US?
LOOKS LIKE HE'S GOING TO GET HIS PERSONAL STEREO REPAIRED!
But—
GLASS BLOWING FACTORY
THIS IS THE PLACE I WANT!
Later—
HOPE IT'S OKAY, KORKY!
JUST WHAT I WANTED, FRED!
HURRAH!
I'VE GOT A NEW PERSONAL STEREO SYSTEM NOW!

DESPERATE
DAN
HOWDY, FOLKS!

It's a quiet day in Cactusville!

But not for long . . .
BANK
BANG! BANG!
STOP, THIEF!
$

Shortly —
THAT'S WHAT THE BANK ROBBER LOOKS LIKE, DAN! I CARVED HIS FACE ON MY TOTEM POLE!
I'LL TRACK DOWN THE CROOK!

THE CROOK HEADED FOR SMALLVILLE, DAN!
AND I'LL TAKE THIS WITH ME, SO I'LL RECOGNISE HIM!

SORRY, DAN! THAT TOTEM POLE'S TOO BIG TO BRING INTO THE TRAIN!
I'LL RIDE TO SMALLVILLE ON THE ROOF!
SHUCKS! I FORGOT ABOUT THAT BRIDGE!
I HAVEN'T TRIED POLE-VAULTING SINCE I BROKE THE POLE AT MY SCHOOL SPORTS!
HERE GOES!

PHEW! MADE IT!
THUD!

But then —
OH, NO! THIS TRAIN AIN'T GOING TO SMALLVILLE!
SMALLVILLE
THE COAST

SMALLVILLE
THE COAST
WELL, YOU DIDN'T EXPECT ME TO WALK, DID YOU?

I'VE REACHED SMALLVILLE AT LAST, BUT IT LOOKS MIGHTY QUIET!
BANK

I'LL TAKE A LOOK AROUND IN CASE THAT CROOK'S STILL HERE!
BANK
$
ANOTHER SUCCESSFUL HOLD-UP!

SLAM!
ULK!
$

I'M MIGHTY SORRY, BUDDY!
HEY! THIS GUY'S THE CROOK!
ANYTHING ELSE I CAN DO TO HELP, SHERIFF?
JAIL
WELL, THAT TOTEM POLE'S JUST WHAT WE NEED FOR A DISPLAY IN THE TOWN MUSEUM!
So—
ITEMS USED TO CATCH CROOKS
WANTED
PETE' KIRTON
FOR
ARMED ROBBERY
$1,000
REWARD
COMPUTER
PHOTO-FIT-KIT
BUT HOW COULD A TOTEM POLE BE USED TO CATCH A CROOK?
WE KNOW THE ANSWER, DON'T WE, READERS?

THE BURRD
IT'S A LONG WALK TO BINKS' STORE FOR THE BIG SALE!
I CAN TAKE A SHORT-CUT BY FLYING THERE!
FLYING IS GREAT!
I HAVE THE FREEDOM OF THE SKIES!
SWOOP!
GET OUT OF MY WAY, YOU FEATHERED PEST!
SQUAWK!
WHUMP!
WELL, FLYING IS PERFECTLY SAFE — APART FROM HANG-GLIDERS, THAT IS!
YAHOO!
THUD!
OOF!
— AND I FORGOT ABOUT SILLY PARACHUTISTS!
SLURP!
EEK! AND HAWKS!
SQUAWK!
AS I WAS SAYING . . .

AARGH! AND NOW A SWARM OF BEES!
Later, at Binks' store—
WHAT HAPPENED, BURRD?
ER, IT'S A LONG STORY!
LET'S GO INTO THE STORE!
BINKS
CONGRATULATIONS! YOU ARE OUR 10,000TH CUSTOMER!
SALE
YOU GET ALL YOUR PURCHASES AT HALF PRICE, AND A FREE FLIGHT HOME IN A HELICOPTER!
COME ON, BURRD! FLY HOME WITH ME!
BINKS
NO FEAR! I'LL WALK!

HAM and EGGHEAD
BOOKWORM
WOULD YOU LIKE TO COME TO MY BIRTHDAY PARTY, EGGHEAD?
OKAY! AFTER I'VE FINISHED READING THIS BOOK ABOUT THE LAW OF GRAVITY!
NEWTON'S LAW of GRAVITY
GRAVITY? WHAT'S THAT?
I'LL SHOW YOU!
WATCH WHAT HAPPENS WHEN I THROW THIS APPLE UP INTO THE AIR!
OUCH!
BONK!
EVERYTHING THAT GOES UP MUST COME DOWN! GRAVITY IS THE REASON!
HOLD IT! I KNOW SOMETHING THAT GOES UP AND NEVER COMES DOWN!
IMPOSSIBLE!
THE NUMBER OF CANDLES ON MY CAKE GOES UP EVERY YEAR AND NEVER COMES DOWN!
OH, NO!
SWOON!

A "FETE" WORSE FOR THE JOCKS AND THE
THE HELTER SKELTER
WAAH!
SKELTER
HAPPY LANDINGS, GEORDIE! HO-HO!
TIPPING THE BED
EEK!
RIGHT ON THE BUTTON!
THROW-ING THE WELLIE
YAHOO!
TOSS
PERHAPS YOU SHOULD HAVE TAKEN THE GEORDIE OUT OF THE WELLIE FIRST, BIG JOCK!
"DON'T" BEAT THE GOALIE
HOWL!
BANG ON TARGET!

THAN DEATH
GEORDIES
THE LUCKY DIP
GASP!
LUCKY DIP
IT'S AN UNLUCKY DIP FOR THAT GEORDIE!
TING A-LING!
OOYAH!
TEST YOUR STRENGTH MACHINE
HA-HA! I CAN HIT THAT BELL EVERY TIME!
THE COCONUT SHY
BET I CAN RAISE MORE BUMPS THAN YOU!
OUCH!
I WANT TO KISS ALL THE BOYS!
HELP! THAT'S DEFINITELY A FATE WORSE THAN DEATH!
CRUMBS!
RUN!
BEAUTY QUEEN

WHEN LITTLE ERIC EATS A BANANA, HE INSTANTLY BECOMES....BANANAMAN!

BANANAMAN'S

FAZZOOOOM!
...CHANGES HIM INTO BANANAMAN!
OH... ER... I'VE TURNED INTO A HEROIC CRIME-FIGHTER! I'LL JUST WAIT BY THE PHONE FOR A CALL! THERE WILL BE LOTS OF PEOPLE WANTING MY HELP!
Days later—
MAYBE I SHOULD TRY THE JOB CENTRE FOR SOME WORK!
Hasn't rung once!
Then—
JOB CENTRE
KRUMP!
THE DOOR'S ROUND THERE, YOU TWIT!
Inside—
I WAS HERE FIRST! I'M AN OUT-OF-WORK LIGHTHOUSE KEEPER AND I WANT THE FIRST JOB!
I'LL SEE IF THEY NEED ANY HELP AT THE BUILDING BLOCK FACTORY THEN!
PEOPLE AREN'T BUYING ENOUGH BUILDING BLOCKS, SO WE'RE ALL GOING TO LOSE OUR JOBS!
BUILDING BLOCK FACTORY
CLOSING DOWN
OH, NO! THAT'S TERRIBLE!

NOW, THERE'S SOMEONE WHO'S BUSY!
CRASH HELMETS FOR SALE
EVERYONE AROUND HERE HAS TO WEAR A HELMET! BITS OF ROCK AND METAL KEEP DROPPING FROM SPACE!
HMM! THIS IS A JOB FOR... ME!
So, out in space—
I'LL ASK A POLICEMAN WHAT'S GOING ON!
THAT ASTEROID IS RIGHT IN THE MIDDLE OF THE MILKY MOTORWAY! IT'S CAUSING A LOT OF CRASHES!
MAYBE I CAN HELP, OFFICER!
Back on Earth—
OPEN UP THE FACTORY! I'VE A BIG ORDER FOR YOU!
ORDER
SIX MILLION GIANT BUILDING BLOCKS
GASP!
BUILDING BLOCK FACTORY
KEEP THE BUILDING BLOCKS COMING! I'M A FAST WORKER!
EH? THAT WASN'T THERE FIVE MINUTES AGO!

WHEN'S HE GOING TO STOP?
AND NOW TO POP THE TOP ON.
WE'RE SO FAR UP, MY CRISPS ARE WEIGHTLESS!

THANKS, BANANAMAN! NOW I CAN WORK AS A LIGHTHOUSE KEEPER AGAIN!
AND THAT LIGHTHOUSE WILL STOP THINGS CRASHING INTO THE ASTEROID!
SPACE IS A SAFER PLACE FOR DRIVERS, NOW!
Er, apart from the drivers who've had to swerve to avoid hitting YOU, Bananaman!

I FOUND WORK FOR THE LIGHTHOUSE KEEPER AND THE BUILDING BLOCK MAKERS! EVERYONE WILL BE HAPPY NOW...
...EXCEPT HIM!
TWIT! NOW YOU'VE PUT UP THAT LIGHTHOUSE...

...NO ONE WANTS TO BUY MY CRASH HELMETS ANY MORE!

What's this? Has Bananaman started making model lions?

No! It's a real lion! And Bananaman's trying to keep it quiet!
SSH! DON'T GIVE AWAY MY HIDING PLACE!
WHERE'S THAT BANANA-BRAINED BUFFOON?

Dimples
ME THINK ME'S GOING TO SNEEZE...
I'M FEELING REALLY FIT FOR THE FUN RUN TODAY!
AATISHOO!
YAHOO!
YOU'VE GOT A BAD COLD — DON'T PASS IT ON TO ME!
PUT THIS PEG ON YOUR NOSE. I CAN'T TAKE THE RISK OF CATCHING YOUR GERMS!
DAD'S BEING REALLY SILLY NOW!
STAY IN YOUR BEDROOM, DIMPLES! THAT'LL STOP YOU SPREADING GERMS!

BASH!
ME HASN'T GOT A COLD. IF YOU KEEP ME IN HERE, ME WILL YELL ALL DAY LONG!
OKAY! THERE'S ONLY ONE THING FOR IT!

BAH! ME HAS TO WEAR THIS SPACE-SUIT!

ME KEEP TELLING YOU — ME HASN'T GOT A COLD!
BUT YOU SNEEZED!

YES, 'COS ME'S BEEN PLAYING WITH MY SNEEZING POWDER!
S-S-S-SNEEZING POWDER?
SNEEZING POWDER

WANT SOME, DADDY?
NO! KEEP AWAY!

Meanwhile —
FUN RUN START
READY? GET SET —
GO!
POP!
GANGWAY!
YAHOO!
GASP! PUFF! I'VE RUN FOR MILES, AND I STILL CAN'T SHAKE HIM OFF!
HAVE A SNIFF!
DAD WAS IN SUCH A HURRY TO ESCAPE ME — HE WON THE FUN RUN!
SPLOOSH!
AND ME WON THE TROPHY FOR THE MOST UNUSUAL FUN RUN OUTFIT!
G#!*#! *☆#!?!
HO-HO!

BULLY BEEF and CHIPS
I'LL BE BACK IN A MINUTE, BOYS! MEANWHILE CHECK THAT ALL THE GEAR IS OKAY!
MOUNTAIN-EERING CLUB
AHA!
LEAVE IT TO US!

CLUB
HI, LADS! I'LL GIVE YOU A HAND!
OH, NO— IT'S BEEFY.

ARE THESE SAUCEPANS SOUND?

YES THEY SOUND FINE!
OOH!
DONG!
DONG!
OUCH!

NOW, HOW ARE THE ROPES?
OOH!
AAH!

FINE — THIS ONE IS STRONG.
GASP!
GASP!
HAVE A SEAT!
NO!
SHOVE!
EEK!
THE CRAMPONS ARE SHARP!
Later—
I'LL BET BEEFY IS TOO FAT TO GET INTO THIS SLEEPING-BAG.
I'LL BET HE ISN'T.
FAT, EH? I'LL SHOW YOU.
QUICK, PULL THE DRAW-STRINGS.
GOT HIM.
HEY!
NOW, WE'LL TEST THE SKI-STICKS!
GOOD IDEA.
THESE STICKS ARE CERTAINLY SHARP ENOUGH!
HELP!
PROD!
HOP!

THE SMASHER
BET YOU CAN'T SCORE A GOAL, SMASHER!
OH, NO? JUST WATCH!

OO-ER! I'VE HIT THAT GREENHOUSE!
KICK!
CRASH!
GOSH!

GURR! I SAW WHO DID THAT, SMASHER! I KNOW WHERE TO SEND THE BILL!

Later, at home—
BAH! I'M FED UP RECEIVING THESE BILLS!
BILL

GIVE ME YOUR FOOTBALL. I'M GOING TO LOCK IT AWAY!
AW, DAD!

Later—
WE MUST TRY TO STOP SMASHER PLAYING FOOTBALL, DAD.
I'VE GOT AN IDEA, MUM! WE'LL GIVE HIM A REFEREE'S KIT! IF HE'S REFEREEING A GAME, HE WON'T BE KICKING THE BALL!

So—
HERE'S A PRESENT FOR YOU, SMASHER!
COO! THANKS, DAD!
NOTE BOOK

MUST TRY THE WHISTLE FIRST—

PHEEP
AARGH!
YOW!
CRASH!

JEEPERS! MUST DASH!
GURR!
COME BACK, SMASHER!

PHEW! I'VE SHAKEN 'EM OFF! NOW FOR SOME FUN WITH THE REFEREE'S COIN!

JUST HEAT IT OVER THIS BRAZIER—

— AND DROP IT ON THE PAVEMENT, SO—

GOSH! A COIN!

THIS IS MY LUCKY DAY—
WAIT FOR IT—

HA-HA!
YEEARGH!

OW! SO THAT WAS YOUR TRICK, SMASHER!
TIME TO GO AGAIN!
Later—
NOW FOR SOME FUN WITH THE REFEREE'S PENCIL!
AH! HERE'S A CHANCE!
DRINK
Fizz-Fizz

HOI!
DRINK
Fizz-Fizz
Bobo Baby Powder
REDDO LIP
I ONLY STUCK UP THESE POSTERS HALF AN HOUR AGO!
EEK!

GURR! I'M GOING TO TELL YOUR DAD ABOUT THIS, SMASHER!
Much later, after more pranks—
YIPPEE! WHAT GREAT FUN I'VE HAD! NOW IT'S TIME FOR TEA!

OH-OH!
GROAN!
BILLS

PLEASE TAKE YOUR FOOTBALL BACK — IT'LL BE CHEAPER FOR ME!
I'LL THINK ABOUT IT!
BILLS

THE SNOBBS and

THE SNOBBS' HOUSE

THE SNOBBS' BEDROOM

THE SNOBBS' BATHROOM

THE SNOBBS' KITCHEN

THE SNOBBS' LOUNGE

THE SLOBBS

THE SLOBBS' HOUSE

CONTINUED OVERLEAF

At the Snobbs' house —
THAT'S YOUR MAIL!
At the Slobbs' house —
ONLY ONE LETTER FOR YOU!
LOOK AT ALL THESE BILLS! ELECTRICITY — £300, BUTCHER — £50, VIDEO HIRE — £40, TELEPHONE — £80. THIS IS TERRIBLE! I DON'T FEEL HUNGRY ANY MORE!
ONLY ONE BILL — FIFTY PENCE FOR A CANDLE! WE CAN EASILY AFFORD THAT! OH, HAPPY DAYS!

DANDY HORSELAUGHS

The JOCKS AND THE GEORDIES
In the playpark—
OOYAH!
YAHOO!
WAAH!
PUSH
SNIP!
TWANG!
OOF!
GOTCHA!
THUD!

HOI! STOP THIS NONSENSE!

CLEAR OFF! AND DON'T COME BACK!
OUCH!
BIFF!
RUN!

Later—
THAT'S THE BACKYARD OF THE TRICK SHOP!
WONDER WHAT'S IN THOSE BOXES?

JINGS! INFLATABLE RUBBER ANIMALS!
WE COULD HAVE SOME FUN WITH THESE!

Shortly—
KEEP OUT
YUMMY! THOSE APPLES LOOK DELICIOUS!

I'LL JUST HELP MYSELF TO ONE OR TWO — OR MAYBE TEN!

EEK! A G-GORILLA!

HELP!

HO-HO! OUR INFLATABLE GORILLA MADE A MONKEY OUT OF HIM!
PULL
CHUCKLE!

A little later—
TEE-HEE! I'VE JUST HAD ANOTHER IDEA!

A few moments later—
HOI! LEAVE OUR FOOTBALL ALONE!

BAH! IT WENT INTO THESE BUSHES!

WAAH! AT-T-T-TIGER!
ROAR!

HELP!
HO-HO! THAT WORKED A TREAT!
ROAR!
AYE, AND THIS TAPE RECORDING HELPED TOO!

Later—
THIS IS GREAT FUN!

WHEE!

EEK! A RHINO!

WOW! JUST MANAGED TO SWERVE IN TIME!

YAHOO! – GLUB!
SPLOOSH!

FASTER, LANKY! IT'S AFTER YOU! HO-HO!

Then, outside the park keeper's shed—
HEY, GEORDIE! I CHALLENGE YOU TO A BEAR-HUGGING CONTEST!

DON'T MAKE ME LAUGH, ECK! I'D CRUSH YOU LIKE A GRAPE!
OH, IT'S NOT ME YOU'LL BE BEAR-HUGGING—

IT'S HIM!
GROWL!
EEK! A GRIZZLY B-B-BEAR!

WAAH!
HA-HA! WHAT A LAUGH!

WE'VE BEEN CATCHING OUT THE GEORDIES ONE AT A TIME, BUT WITH MY NEW PLAN, WE'LL DEAL WITH THEM ALL AT ONCE!

So—
FIRST, WE'LL ANCHOR THE PLAYPARK CASTLE TO THIS TREE, AND THEN—

—WE'LL TIE ONE OF THE INFLATABLE ANIMALS TO EACH OF THE FOUR CASTLE TURRETS!
RIGHTO, BIG JOCK!

NOW WE FILL THE SKINS WITH LIGHTER-THAN-AIR-GAS!
GAS

CUT
HOLD ON, JOCKS!

WE HAVE LIFT-OFF!
JINGS! WE CAN SEE FOR MILES FROM UP HERE!
HURRAH!
THIS IS BRAW!

AND THERE ARE THE GEORDIES! LET 'EM HAVE IT, JOCKS!
BANG ON TARGET!
RUN, LADS! OOYAH!
SPLAT!
AARGH!
GROOGH!
OOF!

LUCKY I'M NEAR MY HOUSE!

THIS IS WHEN MY REMOTE CONTROL 'PLANE WILL COME IN HANDY!

THE JOCKS HAVE HAD IT NOW! TEE-HEE!

ZOOM!
TEAR!

HISS!
RIP!
WOW!

HISS!
HISS!
HISS!
HISS!
EEK! THE GAS IS ESCAPING FAST!
OH, NO! WE'RE LANDING IN THE ZOO!

EEK! WE'VE LANDED IN THE MIDDLE OF THE LIONS' DEN!
GURR! I WANT MY CASTLE BACK!
YOU'VE RUINED MY INFLATABLE ANIMALS! I'LL TAKE IT OUT OF YOUR HIDES!
OH, MOTHER!
WE'LL HELP YOU OUT, BIG JOCK!
ROAR!
GULP! MAYBE WE'RE SAFER HERE WITH THE LIONS!
GROWL!
SNARL!
HOWL!
WAH!
WHAT A BRAVE STUNT!

HARRY AND HIS HIPPO
GET THAT USELESS FAT LUMP OUT OF HERE!
OO . . . ER!
THE FIRE BRIGADE! THAT'S FOR ME!
JOIN THE FIRE BRIGADE
So—
HM! HE'S A BIT FAT!
CHIEF
FIRST, YOU'LL HAVE TO LEARN TO CLIMB LADDERS. LIKE THIS.
And—
THIS IS EASY!
ULP!
CRACK!

EEK! I'M TOO FAT!
OOF!
GRR! LET'S SEE HOW YOU HANDLE A HOSE INSTEAD!
THE USELESS FAT LUMP! HE'S MADE A MUD BATH!
WHOOOSH!
JUST SPRAY IT ON THE GROUND!
SPLAT!
WAHEY! I LOVE A WALLOW!

SNARL! CLEAR OFF!
SNIFF! MAYBE I AM A USELESS FAT LUMP! SOB!

Then—
CLANG! CLANG! CLANG! CLANG!
WOW! THERE MUST BE A FIRE SOMEWHERE!

OH, NO! THERE'S A HOLE IN OUR SAFETY SHEET AND THAT LITTLE GIRL IS TRAPPED! SHE CAN'T JUMP!
HELP! HELP!

WHAT'S HIPPO UP TO?
ALLOW ME!

FLUMP!
YIPPEE! I'M SAFE! GOOD OLD HIPPO!

WHO'S A USELESS FAT LUMP NOW, EH?
BLUSH!
BEAM!

WHEN I GROW UP I WOULD LIKE TO BE A DOOR-TO-DOOR SALESMAN!
EXCUSE ME, MADAM! WOULD YOU LIKE TO BUY A DOOR?
OH, NO!
HAM
WHEN I GROW UP I WOULD LIKE TO BE A SPACE-CRAFT PILOT!
ANYTHING TO GET AWAY FROM THAT FOOL HAM!
EGG-HEAD
WHEN I GROW UP I WOULD LIKE TO BE A STILT-WALKER!
NOW I'M AS BIG AS EVERYONE ELSE!
WHEN I
DIMPLES
SMASHER
WHEN I GROW UP I WOULD LIKE TO BE AN AUCTIONEER!
SMASH!
GOING GOING, GONE —

BULLY BEEF
SPLOOSH!
WHEN I GROW UP I WOULD LIKE TO BE A RACING CAR DRIVER!
WHEN I GROW UP I WOULD LIKE TO BE A TRAFFIC WARDEN.
PARKING TICKET
CHIPS
GROW UP
ZOO
WHEN I GROW UP I WOULD LIKE TO BE A ZOO-KEEPER!
DINAH MO
GEORDIES' HUT
WHEN I GROW UP I WOULD LIKE TO BE A TRUANT-CATCHER!
BIG JOCK

MY PAL OZZIE
ITTER
MARK BARTON was an ace jockey, but he was also a jockey with a difference! For when young Mark cleared the jumps at his uncle's safari park, he was riding an . . . OSTRICH!

After clearing the last jump, Mark headed into the country.
COME ON, OZZIE! LET'S GO FOR A RUN!

But, suddenly —
OH, NO! THAT CAR'S GOING MUCH TOO FAST FOR A ROAD LIKE THIS!

And, Mark knew that only one man would drive so recklessly — Ron Grimshaw, a local builder.
GRIMSHAW'S A FOOL! HE'S SCARED THE LIFE OUT OF OZZIE!

No amount of coaxing could stop the terrified bird!
OOF!

But his accident was soon forgotten when Mark overheard a sinister conversation.
THAT'S SETTLED, THEN! WE SNATCH THE PRINCESS AT TWO O'CLOCK ON FRIDAY!

As they went their separate ways, the men had no idea they'd been overheard.

COME ON, OZZIE! WE'VE GOT TO TELL THE COPS ABOUT THIS!

HOI! YOU CAN'T PARK YOUR OSTRICH HERE! THIS AREA'S RESERVED FOR POLICE VEHICLES!
PUSH
THIS IS AN EMERGENCY! I'LL BE AS QUICK AS I CAN, OFFICER!

Inside —
WANTED
. . . AND THEY SAID THEY WERE GOING TO SNATCH THE PRINCESS AT TWO, ON FRIDAY!
THERE ARE NO ROYAL VISITS TO THIS AREA PLANNED FOR MONTHS! NOW PUSH OFF AND STOP WASTING OUR TIME.

When the police didn't believe his story, Mark felt pretty low, but the news that greeted him back at his uncle's safari park made him feel even worse.
SORRY, MARK! I NEED £5,000 TO KEEP THE PARK GOING, AND I DON'T HAVE THE CASH!
THAT'S TERRIBLE, UNCLE!
GLENDALE SAFARI PARK
WILL BE SOLD BY AUCTION ON FRIDAY
Ron Grimshaw was quick to hear about the safari park's problems.

THAT'S THE BEST NEWS I'VE HEARD FOR AGES! I'M GOING TO BUY THIS PARK AND BUILD AN OFFICE BLOCK ON IT!
SHOVE OFF, GRIMSHAW! YOU DON'T OWN THIS GROUND YET!
GLENDALE SAFARI·PA
WILL BE SO
BY AUCTION
ON FRIDAY

I'M AFRAID OZZIE WILL HAVE TO GO AS WELL, MARK, BUT I'VE FOUND A GOOD HOME FOR HIM! YOU CAN DELIVER OZZIE ON FRIDAY!

On Friday morning Mark decided to have a long lie . . .

. . . but Ozzie had other ideas!
CUT THAT OUT, OZZIE! YOU'RE WORSE THAN A COCKEREL!

Later that day, there were a lot of long faces at the safari park when it was time to take Ozzie to his new home.
TIM WILL DRIVE YOU THERE, MARK!
COME ON, OZZIE! WE MIGHT AS WELL GET THIS OVER WITH!

GLENDALE SAFARI PARK
CHEERIO, MARK! BY THE TIME YOU RETURN, THE SAFARI PARK WILL HAVE BEEN SOLD!

But they'd no sooner left the park when Mark and Ozzie found themselves in a monster traffic jam. And to make matters worse, heading in the opposite direction in his flashy car . . .

. . . was Ron Grimshaw!
WE MEET AGAIN, YOUNG BARTON! I'M OFF TO THE AUCTION TO BUY THE SAFARI PARK AND THERE'S NOTHING YOUR UNCLE CAN DO ABOUT IT!
SLOW
BUZZ OFF, GRIMSHAW!

Ozzie hadn't forgotten the scare Grimshaw had given him in the woods, and now the bird saw a chance for revenge.
HEY! WHAT'S THE BIG IDEA?

IT'S LUCKY FOR YOU YOU'RE NOT UP FOR SALE, BIRDY! I'D HAVE BOUGHT YOU FOR MY SUNDAY LUNCH!
SWITCH ON THE RADIO, TIM, SO WE DON'T HEAR THAT YELLING!

THE INCAN PRINCESS GOLD STATUE ARRIVES AT THE CITY MUSEUM TODAY!
THAT'S THE PRINCESS THOSE CROOKS ARE GOING TO SNATCH!

WE'LL NEVER REACH THE POLICE STATION IN TIME BECAUSE OF ALL THE TRAFFIC! I'LL BE QUICKER ON OZZIE!
BUT IF THE POLICE DIDN'T BELIEVE YOU LAST TIME, WHY SHOULD THEY NOW, MARK?

THEY'LL BELIEVE ME! I'LL MAKE SURE OF THAT!

At the Police Station —
I HAVE AN IMPORTANT MESSAGE FOR THE CHIEF INSPECTOR!
YOU CAN'T SEE HIM! HE'S HAVING LUNCH!

HOLD IT! YOU CAN'T GO IN THERE!
CANTEEN
PUSH
PUSH

But that's exactly where Mark and Ozzie did go! And the long-legged bird made a bee-line for the Chief Inspector's plate!

TODAY'S
MENU

Mark's plan worked perfectly. As Ozzie galloped from the police station, the cops came dashing in pursuit!
POLICE

KEEP GOING, OZZIE! WE'RE ALMOST AT THE MUSEUM.

And when the police cars screeched to a halt outside the museum, they discovered there were bigger villains around than Mark and Ozzie.
QUICK! THOSE GUYS ARE STEALING THE INCAN PRINCESS STATUE!
MUSEUM
POLICE

Realising they'd been caught red-handed the thieves gave up.
WELL DONE, LAD! THAT STATUE WAS LOANED TO THE MUSEUM BY RODNEY MAXFIELD, THE MILLIONAIRE!
MUSEUM

And when Mr Maxfield heard about Mark's quick-thinking, he rushed to the police station.
THIS CHEQUE'S FOR YOU, MARK! YOU DESERVE IT FOR SAVING MY STATUE!

Mark knew exactly what he'd like to do with the reward money, but time was running out.
I MUST RUSH! I HAVE TO BE AT AN AUCTION AT FOUR O'CLOCK!
PUSH

But a little farther on —
DISCO
OH, NO! THE LOCK GATES ARE OPEN, OZZIE! AND WE'VE GOT TO CROSS THAT CANAL!

Mark and Ozzie didn't stop when they reached the canal. Instead, they tried their most daring piece of show-jumping ever!
WELL DONE, KID!
GREAT JUMP, OZZIE!

GLENDALE SAFARI PARK AUCTION
TODAY
But at the auction, it looked as if Mark was going to be too late!
...AND THE HIGHEST BID IS FROM MR GRIMSHAW! NO MORE BIDS?...GOING... GOING...

But suddenly—
STOP THE SALE! WE HAVE THE CASH TO SAVE THE PARK, UNCLE!

THANKS A MILLION, MARK! I'M GOING TO MAKE YOU A PARTNER IN THE SAFARI PARK!
INTERFERING KID! I'LL TEACH YOU NOT TO SPOIL MY PLANS!

But Ozzie rushed to Mark's rescue!
OOYAH! OKAY! I'M GOING! I'M GOING!
HE WON'T BOTHER US AGAIN, UNCLE!

DESPERATE DAN
I'M IN THE MOOD FOR FUN!
CACTUSVILLE PARK
YIPPEE!
BOUNCE!
ME NEXT!
WHEE!
BOUNCE!

ULP! IT ISN'T STRONG ENOUGH!
RRRIP!
SLAM!
So—
NOT TO WORRY— I'VE GOT AN IDEA!
CRATER MOUNTAIN

BOOM!
BOOM!
BOOM!
BOOM!
SEE? I'VE MADE MY OWN TRAMPOLINE, AND I'M NOT DOING ANY HARM!
BOOM!
DAN MUST BE JOKING!
EH?
STOP, DAN! THE RED INDIANS MISTOOK YOUR TRAMPOLINING FOR WAR DRUMS— THEY THINK YOU'VE DECLARED WAR!
ER — SORRY ABOUT THAT — ALL A BIG MISTAKE.

WELL DONE, DAN — YOU'VE MADE PEACE WITH THE INDIANS.
YES . . .
BOOM! BOOM! BOOM!
. . . BUT I HAD TO GIVE THEM MY TRAMPOLINE — NOW I HAVE NOWHERE TO BOUNCE!
Soon —
I'VE GOT ANOTHER IDEA.
AIRSHIP HANGAR
BOUNCE!
LOOK! I'M BOUNCING AGAIN!

BOUNCE!
CAREFUL, DAN — DON'T BOUNCE TOO HIGH!

YIKES! TOO LATE!
WHUMPH!
POW!
THE BUNG HAS SHOT OUT!

CHILDREN'S NURSERY
SMASH!
CRASH!
CRASH!
CLANG!
Inside the nursery —
THAT NOISE WOKE UP EVERY CHILD!
IT WAS DESPERATE DAN — I'M GOING TO FETCH HIM!
BOO-HOO!
HOWL!
WAH!
WAIL!
So —
THAT'S A GREAT BIT OF BOUNCING, DAN!
GROAN!
BOUNCE!
BOUNCE!
BOUNCE!
AND YOU'LL KEEP BOUNCING THEM TILL THEY'RE ALL ASLEEP!

THE SMASHER
HI, SAMMY! WHAT'S THAT YOU'VE GOT?
IT'S A LIBRARY BOOK ABOUT HYPNOTISM, SMASHER!
HYPNOTISM

I'VE BEEN PRACTISING A LOT — I'LL TRY IT OUT ON YOU — NOW LET ME SEE... AH, YES!
HO-HO! THAT'S WHAT HE THINKS!
WINK!
HYPNOTISM

SHAZAM! SHAZOO! SHAZOG! NOW YOU THINK YOU ARE A DOG!
HYPNOTISM

BARK! BARK! BARK!
WOW! IT WORKED.
HYPNOTISM

YEEOW!
BITE!

BAH! COME OUT OF THE TRANCE — NOW!
SNAP!
I'LL TRY AGAIN. — AH —
HYPNOTISM

KHAZAM! KHAZOO! KHAZOG! NOW YOU THINK YOU ARE A FROG.

HOP! HOP! HOP!
GREAT! YOU'RE JUST LIKE A FROG.
HYPNOTISM

OOF!
WHUMP!
HYPNOTISM

GRR! YOU CAN COME OUT OF THAT TRANCE NOW.
SNAP!

BAZAM! BAZOO! BAZARROT! NOW YOU THINK YOU ARE A PARROT.

SQUAWK! SQUAWK!

SQUAWK! SQUAWK!
HO-HO! HE'S HEADING FOR THAT TREE!
HYPNOTISM

HEE-HEE! HE'S LOOKING FOR A PERCH.
HYPNOTISM

PRETTY POLLY! PRETTY POLLY!
HEH-HEH!

HMM! I KNOW THAT MAN!

PRETTY POLLY! SAM'S LIBRARY BOOK IS OVERDUE — SAM'S LIBRARY BOOK IS OVERDUE.

HA-HA-HA!
COME WITH ME, BOY!
EEK! IT'S THE LOCAL LIBRARIAN!

Then —
EEK!
CRACK!

HELP!

PHEW! SAVED!
CATCH!

BAH!
LOOK, MUM! THAT BOY THINKS HE'S A MONKEY!

Dimples says
PUFF!
ARGH!
PUFF!
WHEN WEATHERMAN MAKES THINGS HOT, BANANAMAN COOLS THINGS DOWN BY BLOWING AWAY THE WEATHERSHIP!
AND IF DAD'S SOUP IS TOO HOT, ME CAN COOL IT DOWN TOO!
CRACK!
THANKS, BANANAMAN! I'D LOST MY KEY!
BANANAMAN CAN OPEN BANKS WITHOUT A KEY!
AND ME CAN OPEN MY BANKIE WITHOUT A KEY, TOO!

"ME CAN BE LIKE BANANAMAN"
BANANAMAN CAN PUT BADDIES BEHIND BARS!
AND ME CAN PUT DADDIES BEHIND BARS!
FAZZ-
BANANAMAN CAN CHANGE INTO LITTLE ERIC!
PHO-
OOM!
AND I CAN CHANGE DIMPLES INTO PYJAMAS!
BOO! GOOD NIGHT, ALL!

WINKER WATSON
THAT'S 3-0 TO US!
GREAT GOAL, WINKER!
BOOT!
AS well as being a world famous schoolboy prankster, Winker Watson was also an ace footballer. Today he was playing for Greytowers School in a league game, and, after yet another mazy dribble, he crashed the ball past the helpless goalkeeper.
At the end of the game, Winker was carried from the pitch shoulder high.
THREE CHEERS FOR WINKER!
Back in the dressing room, all was not laughter and joy, however —
ISN'T IT AWFUL? WE HAVE THE BEST FOOTBALL TEAM — AND THE WORST STRIPS!
POP

Winker and his pal, Tim Trott, set off to have a word with their Form Master, Mr Creep.
LET'S ASK MR CREEP FOR SOME MONEY TO BUY NEW STRIPS!

Creepy was talking to the school cleaner and the boys overheard him —
NO, YOU CAN'T HAVE A RISE— IN FACT, YOU'RE SACKED!
GOSH! CREEPY'S IN A BAD MOOD!

Winker and Tim started to tip-toe away —
LET'S GET OUT OF HERE!
YOU BOYS— COME HERE AT ONCE!

Back in Creepy's office —
TO SAVE THE SCHOOL MONEY, YOU BOYS CAN DO THE CLEANING!

I'M OFF FOR A CUPPA!
ROTTEN OLD SKINFLINT!
Mr CREEP
DUST
DUST

All of a sudden, as Winker dusted one of the wall panels, he hit a hidden switch —
GOSH! A SECRET PANEL! AND LOOK, WHAT'S THIS?
CLICK!

IT'S A SECRET MESSAGE, TIM! IT SAYS, "GRANDFATHER HOLDS THE SECRET TO HAPPINESS AND SUCCESS!" IT MUST MEAN HIDDEN TREASURE!
I'LL TAKE THAT!
It was nasty old Creepy!
YOU'RE DISMISSED, BOYS.
IF THERE'S ANY HIDDEN TREASURE IN GREYTOWERS, I'LL FIND IT MYSELF — AND KEEP IT! NOW LET ME SEE...
PSST! DON'T WORRY, TIM — I MEMORISED THE MESSAGE!
IT MUST MEAN THE BUST OF THE HEADMASTER'S GRANDFATHER!
The bust was in the Headmaster's office, and so was the Head himself.
ZZZZ
IT'S UP ON THE SHELF, WINKER!
Winker reached in at the open window with the set of extending tongs.
QUIETLY DOES IT! ALMOST THERE!
ZZZZ

SLIP
OOPS!
THUD!

Luckily for Winker, the falling bust had knocked out the Headmaster!
THE BUST— IT'S EMPTY!

THE CLUE MUST MEAN ANOTHER "GRANDFATHER" IN THE SCHOOL! COME ON, TIM! LET'S THINK HARD!
TOSS

Moments later, Mr Creep came stealthily on the scene.
I'LL SNEAK UP AND NAB THE BUST FROM THE HEAD'S STUDY!

AH! EXTENDING TONGS! JUST WHAT I NEED!

I'LL EASILY REACH THE BUST WITH THESE!

Just then—
SO IT WAS YOU WHO KNOCKED THAT BUST ON MY HEAD!
EEK! N — NO!
Later —
IT'LL BE THE STATUE OF THE SCHOOL'S FOUNDER'S GRANDFATHER!
Winker and Tim hurried along to the school garden.
THE TREASURE MUST BE UNDER THE STATUE!
TOPPLE
I'LL DIG BESIDE THE STATUE!

AARGH! IT'S TOPPLING OVER!

OH, GOLLY! THE STATUE HAS STABBED CREEPY!
GULP!

PHEW! THE SWORD WENT BETWEEN MR CREEP'S ARM AND HIS BODY! WE WERE WORRIED FOR A MINUTE!

THE TREASURE ISN'T HIDDEN HERE! BAH! I'VE HAD ENOUGH OF YOU TWO PESTS!

JUST A MINUTE— THAT NOISE!
DONG! DONG! DONG!

THE GRANDFATHER CLOCK IN MY STUDY!
THAT'S WHERE THE TREASURE MUST BE!
In Creepy's study —
I'VE FOUND SOMETHING! BUT WHAT IS IT?

But!
BAH! SO THIS IS THE TREASURE!
IT'S THE ANSWERS TO AN EXAM HELD IN 1952!
THEY WOULD HAVE MADE A SCHOOLBOY HAPPY THEN.

TICK-TOCK!
STUPID CLOCK! TAKE IT TO THE DUMP AT ONCE!
TOWN RUBBISH DUMP
AH, WELL! THERE WAS NO TREASURE AFTER ALL. NOW HOW WILL WE GET THE MONEY FOR NEW STRIPS?
JOE'S ANTIQUES
ALL SORTS OF CLOCKS BOUGHT
TOWN RUBBISH DUMP
HANG ON A MINUTE, TIM! CREEPY THINKS THE GRANDFATHER CLOCK IS WORTHLESS — BUT MAYBE IT ISN'T!
YES, THAT GRANDFATHER CLOCK IS A NICE ANTIQUE — I'LL GIVE YOU FIFTY POUNDS FOR IT!
SMART DEAL, WINKER!
With the money made from the sale of the Grandfather clock, Winker was able to buy new strips for the football team. The "grandfather treasure" had certainly brought Winker happiness and success — and puzzled Creepy into the bargain.
WHERE ON EARTH DID THE BOYS GET THE MONEY FOR THESE NEW STRIPS?
SHOOT FOR GOAL, WINKER!

Dinah Mo
I'LL WIN THAT!
Beauty Contest
QUEEN of the FLOAT PARADE
JUDGING TODAY
BUT, MO! YOU'RE NOT A NICE, PRETTY GIRL!

MY MAKE-UP KIT WILL HELP ME TO WIN THE BEAUTY CONTEST!

BUT I WON'T USE IT ON MYSELF!
ERK!
PLOP!

BOO-HOO! NOW I'M IN A MESS!
HEH-HEH! ONE DOWN, TWENTY-NINE TO GO!

So—
COME HERE, CELIA! YOU NEED SOME LIPSTICK!
EH?

BUT I LOOK AWFUL!
EXACTLY!

Next—
TAKE THAT, AND THAT AND . . .

Judging time—
GOSH! WHO CAN WE PICK AS BEAUTY QUEEN?

HELLO, BOYS!
LOOKS LIKE MO IS THE MOST PRESENTABLE GIRL AROUND!

AFTER COUNTING THE VOTES, I REGRET TO ANNOUNCE THAT OUR QUEEN OF THE FLOAT PARADE WILL BE MO!
MO

SOB! THIS IS A DISGRACE TO OUR SCHOOL!

That afternoon —
ZOO
STOP HERE!
1C MO2
MY FIRST TASK IS AT THE ZOO!

THIS WAY FOR YOUR SPECIAL TEA, MADAM!
THANK YOU, PEASANT!

IN HERE, MILADY!
OUT OF MY WAY, GIRL!

EH?
SLAM!

BAH! THE SPECIAL TREAT WAS JOINING THE CHIMPS' TEA-PARTY!
SPLAT!
SERVES MO RIGHT FOR FIXING THE CONTEST.

The DOMES
The Domes from Outer Space are visiting Earth . . .
MUM
ZANDRA
DOME-MESTIC HELPERS
KOOKABILITY THE ROBOT COOKER
ASTRO
DOG FOOD
DAD
LASER, THE ROBOT DOG

One summer evening—
WE'RE TAKING LASER OUT WALKIES, MUM!
SEE YOU LATER, KIDS! WE'RE GOING TO WATCH TV!

GUFFAW!
THIS MUST BE AN EARTH COMEDY SHOW! IT'S SO SILLY!

Look! It's not comedy — it's "One Shepherd And His Sheepdog!"
HOW RIDICULOUS!
WHAT A GIGGLE!

Then—
I'VE LAUGHED SO MUCH, I NEED A DRINK!
Careful, Dad!
DOG FOOD

Too late!
CLUNK!
DOG FOOD

OH, NO! I'VE LANDED ON THE COMPUTER CONTROLS! WHAT WILL HAPPEN NOW?
ZUMP!
Then—
HELP! ALL OUR AUTOMATIC FURNITURE'S GOING CRAZY!
GASP! WHAT HAVE I DONE?
OOH! THEY'RE STAMPEDING OUT THE DOOR! THERE'S GOING TO BE BIG TROUBLE!

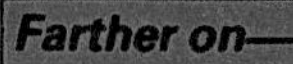
Farther on—

IT'S QUIET TODAY, ASTRO!
YES, ZANDRA!

But then—
DID I SAY QUIET? LOOK OVER THERE?
OH, NO!

OUR FURNITURE'S GONE CRAZY!
WE MUST DO SOMETHING!
WHAP!

AAAAAAAGH!
LEAP!
WOP!

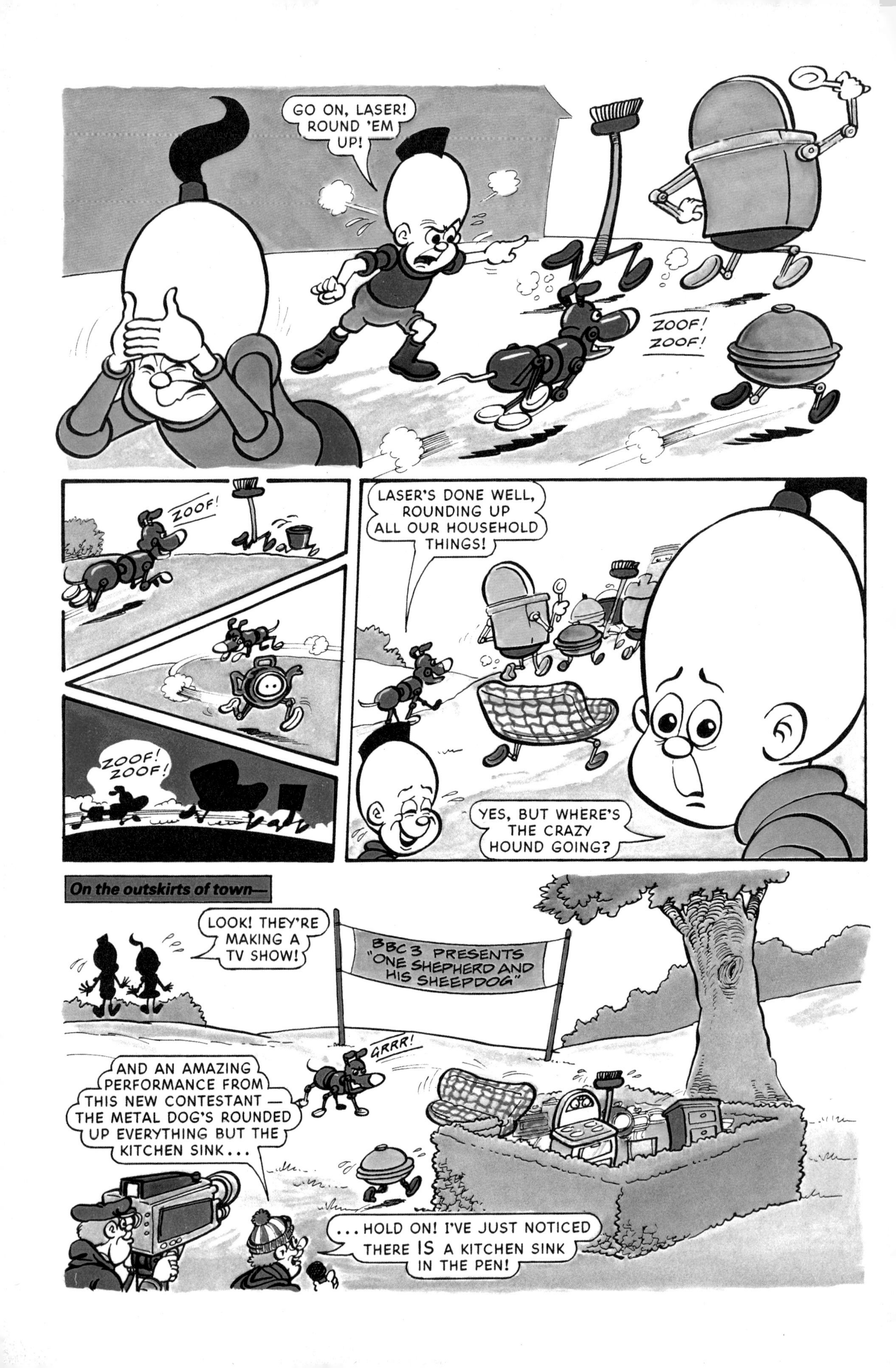
GO ON, LASER! ROUND 'EM UP!
ZOOF! ZOOF!
ZOOF!
ZOOF! ZOOF!
LASER'S DONE WELL, ROUNDING UP ALL OUR HOUSEHOLD THINGS!
YES, BUT WHERE'S THE CRAZY HOUND GOING?
On the outskirts of town—
LOOK! THEY'RE MAKING A TV SHOW!
BBC 3 PRESENTS "ONE SHEPHERD AND HIS SHEEPDOG"
GRRR!
AND AN AMAZING PERFORMANCE FROM THIS NEW CONTESTANT — THE METAL DOG'S ROUNDED UP EVERYTHING BUT THE KITCHEN SINK...
...HOLD ON! I'VE JUST NOTICED THERE IS A KITCHEN SINK IN THE PEN!

Back at the Domes' home—
BUT HOW WILL WE RECOVER ALL OUR THINGS, MUM?
LASER'S DONE THAT FOR US! LOOK AT THE TV, DAD!
. . . AND THE WINNERS OF THIS WEEK'S "ONE SHEPHERD AND HIS SHEEPDOG" ARE ASTRO DOME AND LASER, HIS DOG!
SO, WE'LL GET OUR FURNITURE BACK AND A GOLD CUP! MAYBE THAT ISN'T SUCH A SILLY TV SHOW AFTER ALL!

DANDY HORSELAUGHS

BRASSNECK
YOUNG Charley Brand was an ordinary schoolboy . . . well, almost! For Charley had an amazing metal pal called Brassneck, who could do all sorts of fantastic things.
WE DON'T NEED A GARDEN SPRINKLER WHEN BRASSNECK'S AROUND!
I'M ALWAYS HAPPY TO HELP YOU OUT, CHARLEY!
But suddenly—
YEEEEEK!
ULK! SOUNDS LIKE MUM!
A MOUSE! GET IT OUT OF HERE!

LEAVE THIS TO ME! I KNOW HOW TO GET RID OF MICE!
BRASSNECK'S TURNED HIS NOSE INTO A FLUTE! NOW HE'S LEADING AWAY THAT MOUSE LIKE THE PIED PIPER!

But it wasn't only mice that were attracted by Brassneck's sweet music. Soon every cat and dog for miles around was rushing to follow him!
And they weren't the only creatures to enjoy the flute playing. But Brassneck was too busy concentrating on his performance to notice.
CRASH!
And once the hedge was down, farm animals galore charged out to join the procession.
But then—
HMM! I FORGOT TO ASK CHARLEY WHERE HE WANTED ME TO TAKE THE MOUSE!

Brassneck headed round the block and back towards Charley's house, but he still didn't think to look behind him.
I'VE SEEN A ZEBRA CROSSING BEFORE BUT NEVER A BULL AND A DONKEY!

But back at the house—
BRASSNECK! WHAT'S THE BIG IDEA?
ULP! WHERE DID THEY COME FROM?

And then—
MUM AND DAD ARE COMING BACK FROM THE SHOPS! WE MUST HIDE THOSE ANIMALS!

THAT'S IT, BRASSNECK! BRING OVER THE GARDEN SHED...
... AND WE CAN STICK THE ANIMALS IN THERE, OUT OF SIGHT!
TIME FOR WALKIES, BIG BOY!

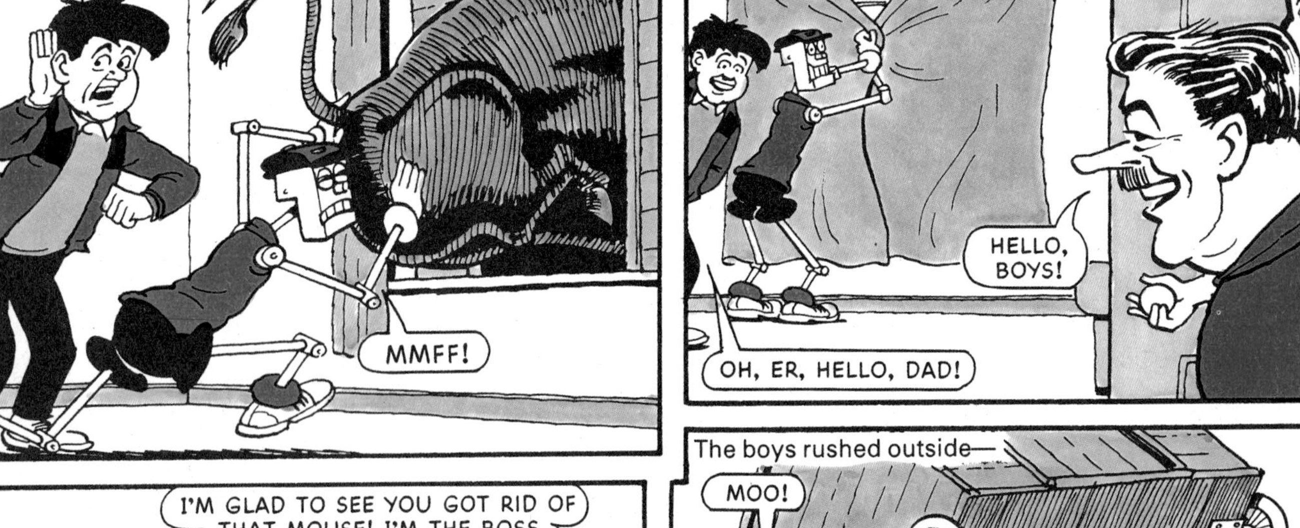
QUICK, BRASSNECK! I CAN HEAR MUM AND DAD COMING IN THE FRONT DOOR!
MMFF!
Seconds later—
HELLO, BOYS!
OH, ER, HELLO, DAD!

I'M GLAD TO SEE YOU GOT RID OF THAT MOUSE! I'M THE BOSS IN THIS HOUSE AND I WON'T ALLOW ANY ANIMALS IN HERE!

The boys rushed outside—
MOO!
HURRY UP AND FIX THOSE WHEELS ON THE SHED, CHARLEY!

GROWL! MOO! NEIGH! MEE-OW!
LET'S GO, BRASSNECK! WE'LL TAKE THOSE ANIMALS BACK TO WHERE THEY CAME FROM!
But the goat reckoned it was feeding time—
CHEW!
SNAP!
OH, NO!
And the runaway shed headed straight back towards Charley's house!
CRASH!
YAAH! WHAT'S HAPPENING?

IT'S OUR GARDEN SHED — AND IT'S FULL OF ANIMALS!
SO, YOU'RE THE BOSS? YOU'RE THE ONE WHO WON'T ALLOW ANIMALS IN THE HOUSE?
WELL, ER . . .
Just then—
YOO-HOO! DO YOU REQUIRE THE SERVICES OF A PIED PIPER?
BRASSNECK! I MIGHT HAVE KNOWN HE'D HAVE SOMETHING TO DO WITH THIS!
RUN, BRASSNECK! DAD'S THE WILDEST CREATURE WE'VE SEEN ALL DAY!
SNARL!
YES, CHARLEY! I DON'T THINK MY NOSE FLUTE WOULD CHARM HIM!

DIMPLES
ME IS THE GREATEST!
ME IS THE NEW CHAMP!
DIMPLES! YOU'VE RUINED THAT TEDDY — NO MORE BOXING!
YOU'D BETTER GET CHANGED INTO YOUR OUTFIT FOR THAT 1950'S PARTY TONIGHT.
YES, DEAR.
Later—
ME IS A SURGEON! ME REPAIR THE ARM OF MY OTHER TEDDY!
BOP!
OOPS! ME PULLED TOO HARD!
TEDDY BOY → OUTFIT
NO MORE TEDDY BEARS — YOU JUST RUIN THEM!

BAH! ROTTEN OLD SPOILSPORT!
YAHOO!
ME NOT HAVE A TEDDY BEAR ANY MORE — BUT NOW ME'S GOT A TEDDY BOY TO PLAY WITH!
HO-HO! DIMPLES IS A LITTLE IMP!

STRANGE HILL SCHOOL
WHAT PANTOMIME WILL WE DO THIS YEAR?

HOW ABOUT CINDERELLA?

I COULD BE CINDERELLA AND THESE TWO COULD BE THE UGLY SISTERS.
NO! THEY'RE TOO HANDSOME!

HOW ABOUT LITTLE RED RIDING HOOD?

I COULD BE THE BIG BAD WOLF.
SNARL
NO! YOU'RE NOT FRIGHTENING ENOUGH.

WHAT ABOUT PETER PAN, SIR?
THAT'S IT! WE'LL HAVE A REHEARSAL!

ULP! I'M SURE I SAW A GHOST A MOMENT AGO!
YIPPEE! I'M CAPTAIN HOOK!
YUMMY!

EEK! I'M HEADING RIGHT FOR THAT CROCODILE!
HO-HO! I DON'T NEED HIDDEN WIRES TO FLY!
THIS SHOW IS A DISASTER! HOW WONDERFUL!
ONE HUNDRED AND EIGH-TY!
EEK!

HAM AND EGGHEAD

Desperate DAN
RATTLESNAKE RINGS
CACTUS SOUP
GRIZZLY STEW
ROCKY MOUNTAIN ROCK CAKES
COW PIE
OWL HOOT JUICE
MATCHES
ZZZZZZ

SHUCKS! IT'S GONE DARK! I WONDER WHAT'S BLOCKING OUT THE LIGHT?

HI, JAKE! WHY ARE YOU WEARING THAT CRAZY HAT?
THERE'S A FUNNY HAT COMPETITION AT THE TOWN HALL, DAN!

SOUNDS LIKE FUN! I'LL FIND A FUNNY HAT AND COME ALONG!

THIS HAT LOOKS SO SILLY, I'M BOUND TO WIN!

HOW DARE YOU, DAN! TAKE OFF MY NEW SUNDAY HAT!
OOF!
SORRY, AUNTIE!

Shortly —
THAT'S WHAT I CALL A FUNNY HAT!
VISIT
LONDON

GREAT HAT, DAN!
COULD BE A WINNER!
JUDGE
YAWN!
EH? WHAT WAS THAT?
JUDGE
OH, NO! IT'S WOKEN UP!
YAH! IT'S NOT A BEARSKIN HAT — IT'S A LIVE BEAR!
OUT, DAN! AND TAKE YOUR HAT WITH YOU!

Then —
SCRAP YARD
HMM! THAT COULD MAKE A FUNNY HAT!
WHAT A FANTASTIC HAT, DAN! IS IT MADE OF CARDBOARD?
NOPE! IT'S METAL! LISTEN!
CLANG! CLANG!
TICK! TICK! TICK!
WHAT'S THAT NOISE?
OOPS! MY TAPPING HAS SET SOMETHING OFF!
WHOOOSH!
CRASH!
TOWN HALL

OUT!!!

Then —
HMM! THAT BARREL WOULD MAKE A FUNNY HAT!

TEXAS TOURING CIRCUS
OH, NO! WHERE HAS OLLIE GONE?

I DIDN'T THINK MY HAT WAS THAT FUNNY!
HA-HA!
HO-HO!

Oh-oh!

NOW WHERE'S THE JUDGE?

HEY! THE JUDGE ISN'T MEANT TO WEAR A FUNNY HAT!
I'VE HAD ENOUGH, DAN! GET OUT . . .
. . . AND TAKE THAT OCTOPUS WITH YOU!
COME ON, BOY!

Shortly —
WHAT'S WRONG, UNCLE DAN?
I'M HAVING TROUBLE WITH HATS!
US TOO!
THE WITCH'S HAT ROUNDABOUT IS BROKEN!

MAYBE I CAN CHEER US ALL UP!

Back at the funny hat competition—
THAT HAT OF YOURS WINS FIRST PRIZE, DAN!

ONLY UNCLE DAN IS TOUGH ENOUGH TO WEAR A WITCH'S HAT ROUNDABOUT!
JUDGE
WELL DONE, DAN!

HOPSCOTCH and MACNAB

WHISK!
BAH! MISSED!
Later—
MY FROG DETECTOR HAS TRACKED DOWN HOPSCOTCH AGAIN. I'LL LASSO HIM THIS TIME.
BLEEP! BLEEP!
BULL'S-EYE!
FOOD, GLORIOUS FOOD—
GULP!
NOW FOR A TASTY FEED! DRAT! THERE'S SOMEONE AT THE DOOR!
I'M THE TV DETECTOR MAN! HAVE YOU GOT A LICENCE FOR YOUR TV SET?
ER, NO!
T.V.
COME ALONG WITH ME, SIR!
MACNAB WON'T BE BACK FOR A LONG TIME, SO I'LL HELP MYSELF TO THE REST OF HIS GRUB.

The JOCKS and the GEORDIES

In the park —

H

OOH!
BASH!
BLAH!
BIFF!

— THE TOY HOUSE WAS A BIG HIT WITH THE KIDS!
OOGLE-SHOOGLE!

WHEE!

YAHOO!
CRASH!

UGGLE-GLUGGLE!
OOGLE-BOOGLE!

— IF ONE OF THEM HAD A TOY, THE OTHER ONE HAD TO HAVE IT TOO!
UGGY-MINE!
GAGA! MINE!

— USUALLY IT ENDED UP WITH NEITHER OF THEM GETTING THE TOY!
YOW!
OUCH!
R-RIP

BOO-HOO! THEY COULDN'T EVEN DRINK THEIR MILK IN PEACE!

— THEY FOUGHT WITH IT!
GLUG!
GLOOB!
SQUIRT SQUIRT

THEY WERE HORRIBLE BABIES BOO-HOO!
WAIL! THEY'RE EVEN WORSE NOW.

— ONLY YESTERDAY I GOT CAUGHT UP IN ONE OF THEIR FIGHTS!
TAKE THAT, YOU SKINNY JOCK — OOPS!
TAKE THAT, YOU FAT GEORDIE PUDDING!
STOP THIS FIGHTING — AARGH!

Back to the present —
THAT WAS A GREAT FIGHT, BIG JOCK!
BRAW!

LOOK AT THEM! IT'S AWFUL!
BOO-HOO!
AYE! YOU KNOW WHAT THEY ARE —

SOB!
BOO-HOO!
— THEY'RE A COUPLE OF BABIES!
HO-HO!

MY BOAT'S A DESTROYER!
TWANG!
HMS SMASHER
HMS
CRASH!
CRASH!
GANG HUT
I HOPE YOU'RE NOT GOING TO DIVE IN THIS THING, HAM!
ME CAN PEDAL REALLY FAST!
WHOOOOSH!
PEDALO
BANANAMAN DOESN'T NEED A BREEZE TO MOVE HIS BANANA BOAT!
BLAST!

BAH! I'M GOING TO CUT THIS CATAMARAN IN HALF!
SPLAT!
SAW! SAW! SAW!
A PIRATE BOAT SUITS ME JUST FINE — WALK THE PLANK, CHIPS!
JAB!
the DANDY BOAT SHOW
HO-HO! MY RAFT HAS ITS OWN FOOD SUPPLY!
TRUST YOU TO BUY US A CHINESE JUNK BOAT!
LIFEBOAT

HALL OF FAME

THEY MUST WANT TO PUT ME IN THE HEROES' HALL OF FAME! THEN I'LL BE REALLY FAMOUS!

AND ROUND HERE WE HAVE...
I THINK I CAN GUESS!
... A LEAKING PIPE! CAN YOU FIX IT FOR ME?
UH?
WHAT A CHEEK! I'LL GO AND DO SOMETHING HEROIC, THEN THEY'LL HAVE TO PUT ME IN THE HEROES' HALL OF FAME!
IT'S GENERAL BLIGHT! I'LL HELP THOSE COPS ARREST HIM!
YOU'LL NEVER TAKE ME, COPPERS!
MY TROUSER RAY WILL FIX YOU!
BLAM!
POW!
BLAST!

SO THAT'S WHAT A TROUSER RAY DOES!
I'M NOT GOING NEAR BLIGHT!
IMAGINE MY PORTRAIT IN THE HALL OF FAME IF HE SHOOTS ME WITH THAT RAY!
COME BACK YOU COWARD, BANANAMAN!
NO FEAR, CHIEF! I'D RATHER LOOK SCARED THAN SILLY!
Farther on —
MR MOLE'S JUST ROBBED A BANK!
I'LL FOLLOW HIM DOWN THE TUNNEL! I'LL ARREST HIM! I'LL BE A HERO!
BUT WAIT! I'LL BE ALL DIRTY!
THEN I'D LOOK A MESS IN THE HEROES' HALL OF FAME! CAN'T HAVE THAT!
SCREECH!

COME BACK AND CATCH THE CROOK, BANANAMAN!
WELL, UNTIE US, AT LEAST!
Farther on —
THAT'S THE HEAVY MOB UP THERE!
I'LL WALK UP AND LISTEN TO THEIR NAUGHTY PLANS!
DO NOT ADJUST YOUR BOOK
THERE'S ONLY ONE SNAG ABOUT BEING ABLE TO WALK UP THE SIDES OF BUILDINGS...
...AND THAT'S PERCHING BIRDS!
SHOO! I'M ON AN IMPORTANT MISSION!

I CAN'T HEAR WHAT THEY'RE SAYING!
I'LL DISGUISE MYSELF AS ONE OF THE GANG...
DISGUISE KIT
...THEN I CAN GO INSIDE AND SPY ON THEM!
NO! I WOULDN'T WANT TO APPEAR LIKE THAT IN THE HALL OF FAME!
DISGUISE KIT
Shortly—
THIS LIBRARY BOOK WAS DUE BACK YESTERDAY!
THIS IS THE CHANCE I'VE BEEN WAITING FOR!
NOW I CAN BE A HERO WITHOUT MESSING UP MY COSTUME!
HOLD IT! FAILING TO RETURN LIBRARY BOOKS ON TIME IS EVIL, WICKED, ER WELL, A TEENY WEENY BIT NAUGHTY ANYWAY!
JUNGLE COOK BY RUDYARD KIPPERING
WELL YOU CAN TAKE IT BACK TO THE LIBRARY, BIG-MOUTH!
JUNGLE COOK BY RUD YARD KIPPERING

YUP! HE REALLY IS A BIG MOUTH!
MMMFFF!!!
JUNGLE COOK BY RUDYARD KIPPERING

I STILL THINK I SHOULD BE IN THE HEROES' HALL OF FAME! I'LL DEMAND I'M GIVEN A PLACE! I'LL ORDER THEM TO INCLUDE ME! I'LL... I'LL, ER... I'LL ASK, THEM NICELY, THAT'S WHAT I'LL DO!

OOH! IF I DON'T GET A PLACE IN THE HALL OF FAME I'LL GO HOME AND SHOUT AT MY GOLDFISH!
HEROES' HALL OF FAME
STOP YAPPING, AND WATCH WHERE YOU'RE FLYING, BANANAMAN!
Reader's voice!

Too late!
CRASH!

DICK TURNIP
WILD BULL HICKOCK
ALEXANDER THE GRAPE
WILLIAM THE CONKER
ERIC COLUMBUS CHRISTOPHER'S ABSENT-MINDED BROTHER, WHO FOUND AMERICA BUT FORGOT WHERE HE PUT IT.
NELSON
HALF NELSON
ULP! WELL, I AM IN THE HEROES' HALL OF FAME AT LAST!
THE BIG DUMPLING CRASHED RIGHT THROUGH THE WALL!

SHERBET
SHERBET HOLMES
MOBY BRICK
HERCULES
RCULES CAN
SO BE SEEN
THE 1ST, 2ND,
D, 4TH, 5TH AND
6TH FLOORS
SIR DANCELOT
THE KNIGHT WHO
COULDN'T STOP
DANCING UNTIL HE GOT
RID OF HIS PLUME
GRANBO

In the library —

THIS'LL DO!

OUT OF THE WAY, PAL!
BASH!
HEY! CAREFUL!

COME IN, NUMBER SEVEN!
SWERVE!
DON'T WORRY! I'LL PAY FOR ANOTHER GO!

WHOOSH-H
IF SHE'S STAYING — I'M GOING!
BONK

I WONDER IF IT GETS AS LONELY AS THIS IN THE ATLANTIC?

After —
I DON'T WANT TO GET SEASICK . . .

. . . THIS WILL GIVE ME PRACTICE FOR WALKING ON A ROLLING DECK.
ROLL
ROLL

OH, NO! IT'S SLIPPED AWAY!
WHEE
ROLL-L

And —
EEK!
WHEEE —

GRR! COME BACK!
NO FEAR!

Back home —
I'LL TRY SLEEPING IN A HAMMOCK!

YIPPEE!
JUMP

EEK!
THUD!

BAH! I'LL PRETEND I'VE BEEN SHIPWRECKED.

The weekend —
I THINK MO'S IN FOR A SURPRISE.
SEASICK PILLS

OH, NO! IT'S A BARGE!
GOOD TO SEE YOU! COME ABOARD!
SEASICK PILLS

KORKY THE CAT

And so —
CAN I INTEREST YOU . . ?
1
HOW STRANGE! I'VE JUST BOUGHT ONE!
At the next flat —
THIS IS THE LATEST IN HAIRBRUSHES —
BUT, I'VE JUST BOUGHT ONE —
A few flats later —
MUMMY HAS JUST BOUGHT ONE OF THESE!
The salesman gives up —
FLATS 1-20
I CAN'T UNDERSTAND IT! I HAVEN'T SOLD A SINGLE BRUSH!
And here's why —
AS YOU CAN SEE, I HAVE A LARGE SELECTION, MADAM!
YES! I'LL HAVE A HAIRBRUSH AND —
BAH! NO WONDER I COULDN'T SELL ANY BRUSHES. KORKY HAS BEEN GETTING TO EVERY FLAT FIRST!
FLATS 1-20
FLATS 21-40
KORKY HELPED ME OUT, SO NOW I'M DOING HIM A FAVOUR!
STREET LIGHT REPAIR CO.

The SMASHER
DUMP
PHOTOS
LOOK! AN OLD PHOTO BOOTH — LET'S HAVE SOME FUN WITH IT!
PHOTO HERE

PUFF!
GASP! IT'S HEAVY!
PANT!
PHOTOS
PHOTO HERE

Later —
NOW WE'VE CLEANED IT UP, IT LOOKS GREAT!
PHOTOS
PHOTO HERE
PHOTOS 10P EACH

DOES IT WORK, SMASHER?
YOU BET! STEP INSIDE AND SIT DOWN!
PHOTO HERE
PHOTOS 10P EACH

Inside —
ARE YOU READY?
YEAH!

GLOOB!
HO-HO!
PRESS
SQUIRT!

BAH! LOOK AT MY FACE!
DON'T WORRY! IT'S ALL PART OF MY NEW PROCESS!

PHOTOS
FIRST WE PUT A CLEAN SHEET OF PAPER ON YOUR FACE...
HEY!

...AND YOU GET YOUR PHOTO! HEE-HEE! WHAT DO YOU EXPECT FOR 10p?

Later —
CAN YOU DO A NICE PHOTO OF ME?
CERTAINLY, JANE — STEP INSIDE!
PHOTOS
TEE-HEE!

RIGHT, NOW WATCH THE BIRDIE!

AARGH!
HO-HO!

SHRIEK!
PHOTOS
PHOTO HERE

Next customer —
SAY CHEESE AND PRESS THAT BUTTON IN FRONT OF YOU!
OKAY!

CHEESE!
PRESS

OOF!
WHUMP!
HA-HA! NOW YOU GET A LUMP OF CHEDDAR ON YOUR NUT!

PHOTOS
THAT WAS A GREAT TRICK!
WHAT A LAUGH!

LET'S CLOSE DOWN FOR LUNCH!
OH-OH! WE'VE GOT MORE CUSTOMERS, BUT THEY DON'T LOOK TOO HAPPY!
CLOSED

THAT'S THEM, CONSTABLE!
PHOTOS
COME BACK HERE!
TIME TO GO!
THEY TRICKED OUR KIDS!

GOTCHA!
GOTCHA!
GOTCHA!
EEK!
GRAB
OO-ER!

At the police station —
HOLD IT!
CLICK! CLICK! CLICK!

Later —
THERE YOU ARE, MY LADS — THESE PHOTOS WILL GO INTO OUR ROGUES' FILE!
OH, DEAR!

DANDY HORSELAUGHS

DESPERATE DAN
LOOK OUT, DAN!
EH?
HOWDY, DAN!
ZOOM!
VROOOOOM!
JUMPING JACKALS! A FLYING BEDSTEAD!

WE'RE ALL ENTERING THE CRAZY FLYING COMPETITION!
THAT SOUNDS LIKE FUN!

Soon, out in the countryside—
CAN I BORROW A FEW THINGS FROM YOU, FARMER BROWN?
SURE, DAN— HELP YOURSELF!

Later—
CLANK!
CLANK!
I'LL HAVE TO PEDAL HARD . . .

ZOOM!
...TO KEEP MY FLYING MACHINE UP IN THE AIR!
DAN BORROWED MY BARN AND WINDMILL!
TOWN HALL
VN H
CHOKE! HE FORGOT TO TAKE OUT THE STRAW!

WALLOP!
TOWN HALL
WHAT WAS THAT? HAS DAN BALED OUT?

NO! THE BIG GALOOT LET A BALE FALL OUT!
HA-HA!
TOWN HALL

Then—
SPLAT!
AND HE'S FORGOTTEN TO TAKE THE HENS OUT!

Up in the flying barn—
HEY! WHAT HAPPENED TO MY EGGS?
MOOOO!
BAA-AAA!
YIKES! MY SHEEP AND COWS ARE STILL IN THE BARN!
OOPS!
I'D BETTER LAND BEFORE THEY ALL FALL OUT!
CLANK! CLANK!
WAIT FOR ME!
HMM! LOTS OF FOLK FLYING AROUND TODAY.
CONTROLLER
YOU CAN'T LAND — WE'RE FULL UP!

NOT TO WORRY—I CAN SEE A PLACE TO LAND!
AGRICULTURAL SHOW GROUND
ZOOM!

DONE IT!
SCREECH!
WOW!

HEY! WHERE DID THAT PESKY HEN COME FROM?

Later—
WELL, I DIDN'T WIN ANYTHING AT THE CRAZY FLYING COMPETITION . . .

. . . BUT I WON SEVERAL PRIZES AT THE AGRICULTURAL SHOW!
BEST COW
BEST BARN DESIGN

Bully Beef and CHIPS
IN
"PRAM WARS"
REMEMBER, I HAVE A JOB FOR YOU THIS AFTERNOON, BEEFY. ONE OF THE PLAYGROUP LADIES NEEDS A BABY-SITTER!
BAH!

HO-HO! I KNOW HOW TO GET IN SOME PRACTICE.

COME HERE, CHIPS! I WANT A WORD WITH YOU!
EEK!

THIS IS WHAT ONE DOES IF A BABY GETS WIND!

THERE! DOES THAT FEEL BETTER, CHIPS? HO-HO!
THUMP! THUMP!
OOF!

NOW TO PUT A NAPPY ON CHIPS — THIS TOWEL WILL DO NICELY!

KEEP STILL, CHIPS!
DOH!
BIFF!

NOW TO HOLD IT WITH A SAFETY PIN!
AARGH!
DUMP
LUCKY I NOTICED THAT OLD PRAM THE OTHER DAY!
PUT ME DOWN, YOU ROTTER!

GURR! WHAT'S THE IDEA, BEEFY?
I DON'T WANT YOU TO FALL OUT, CHIPS!
SEE WHAT I MEAN? THIS IS A VERY BUMPY ROAD.
WAAH! STOPPIT!
SHAKE
RATTLE
BUMP!

CHEERIO, CHIPS!
YAHOO!

AARGH! A PRICKLY BUSH!

ALL RIGHT, YOU BAD BOY! YOU'VE SHOWN ME YOU CAN'T BE A PROPER BABY-SITTER!
DOES THAT MEAN I WON'T HAVE TO DO IT?
So —
CHIPS CAN BABY-SIT INSTEAD. MY RICH FRIEND IS PAYING £10 FOR THE AFTERNOON!
T-TEN POUNDS? OH, NO!
GOSH! THANKS!
VERY WELL, CHIPS — NOW HERE'S WHAT I WANT YOU TO DO —

YOU CAN JOIN THE HAPPY BAND EVERY WEEK!

the Dandy

WEEKLY COMIC is in the shops EVERY TUESDAY

Dimples Daily Dodges
MONDAY
BURST!
PECK!
GLUG!
HA-HA!
THURSDAY
SMELLY SPLODGE!
YAHOO!
FRIDAY
WHIZZZ!!!
YEEAARGH!